MW00958510

OUR
STORY IS
DIFFERENT

A NICU Beginning

PALMETTO
PUBLISHING
Charleston, SC
www.PalmettoPublishing.com

Our Story Is Different
Copyright © 2023 by Shannon Kempton

First Edition

Hardcover ISBN: 979-8-8229-2517-5
Paperback ISBN: 978-9-7988-2292-6

This book is dedicated to
Our NICU Warrior:

_____

_____

To Cameron, our NICU warrior…
May you always be reminded of your strength
and the community that surrounds you.
You are loved beyond words.
To Donovan, the best big brother…
You will always be the brightest light in our darkest days.
To Steve, my rock…
Always & in all ways, my love.

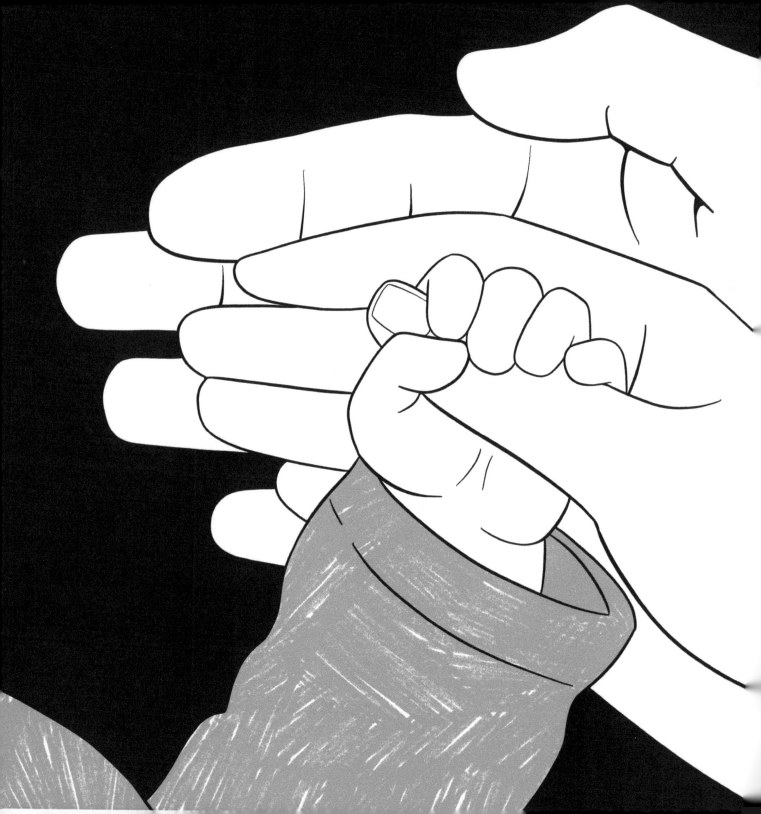

Welcome to the World,
my sweet little one.
This is not what I hoped for you,
A small room with no sun.

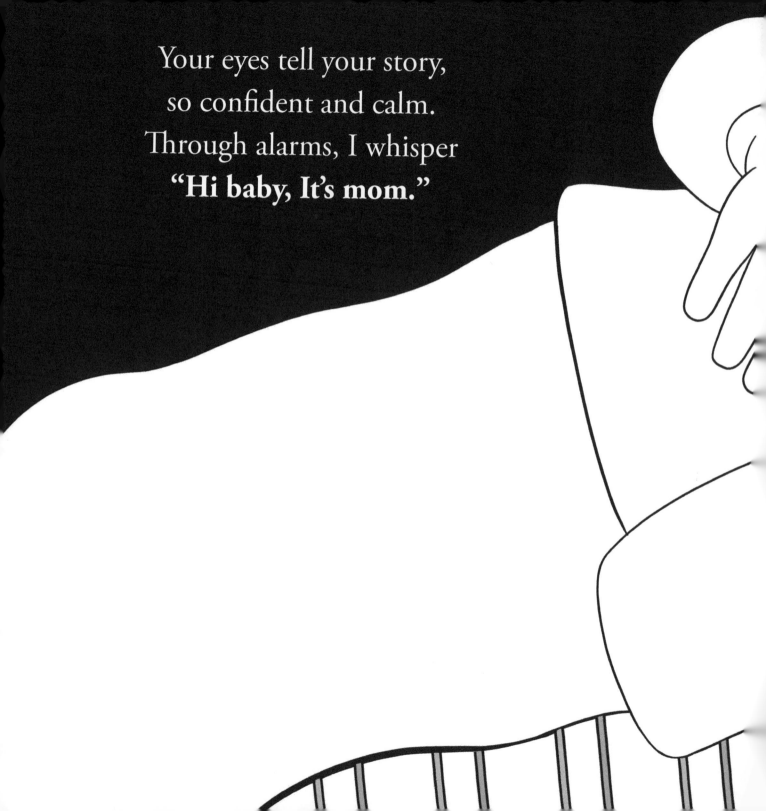

Your eyes tell your story,
so confident and calm.
Through alarms, I whisper
"Hi baby, It's mom."

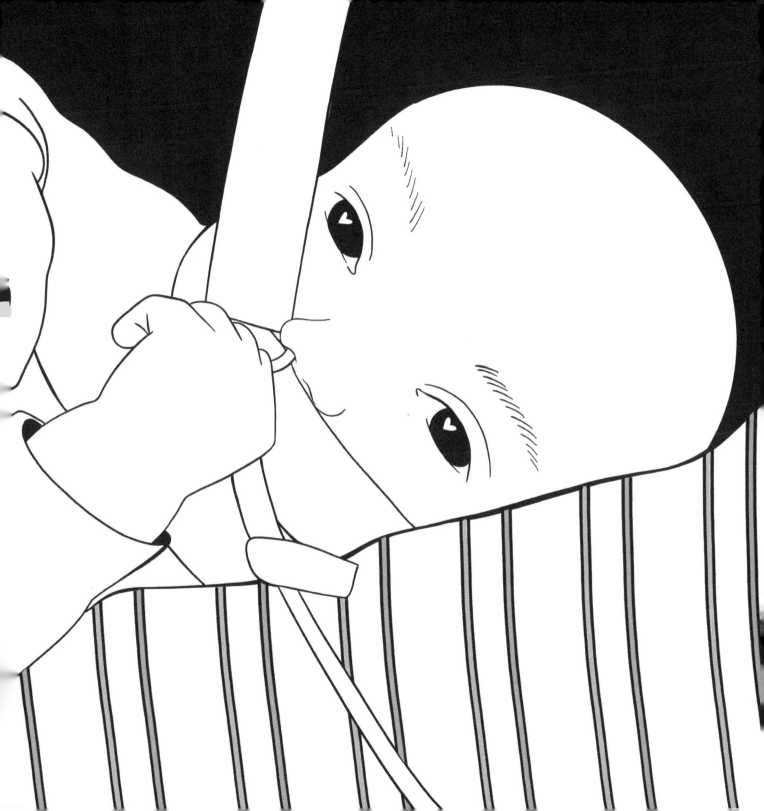

My arms reach out to hold you,
to touch your bare skin.
But all I can do is watch you,
breathe out and breathe in.

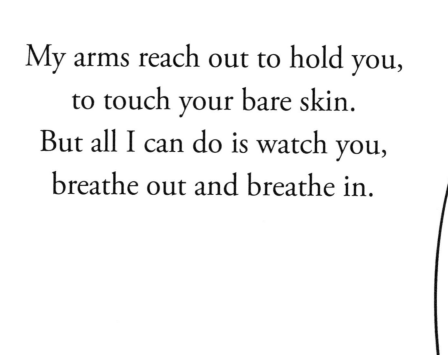

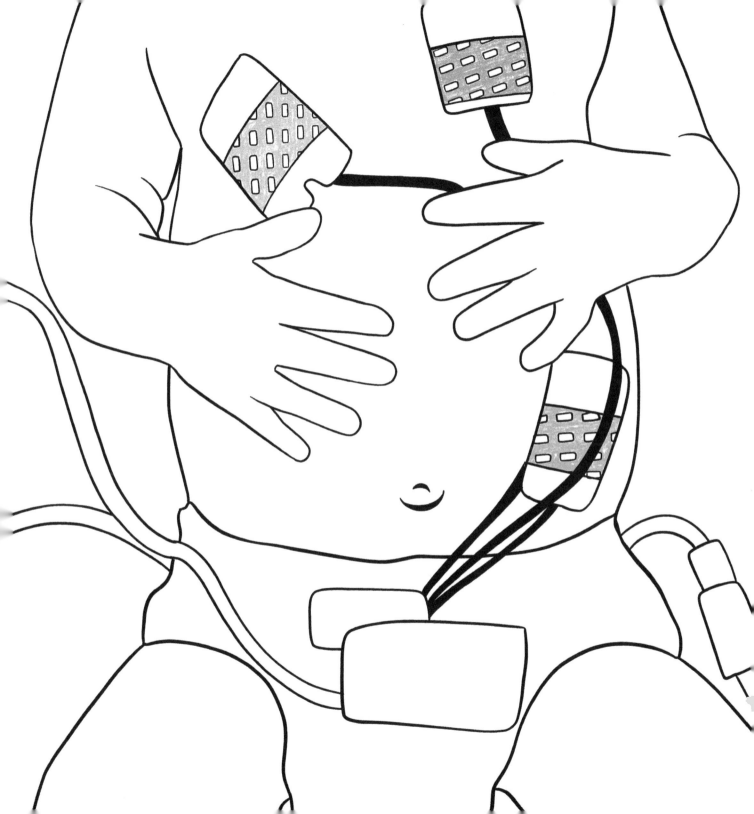

The days seem so long,
yet the hours feel quick.
We sit by your bedside.
We saw your first kick.

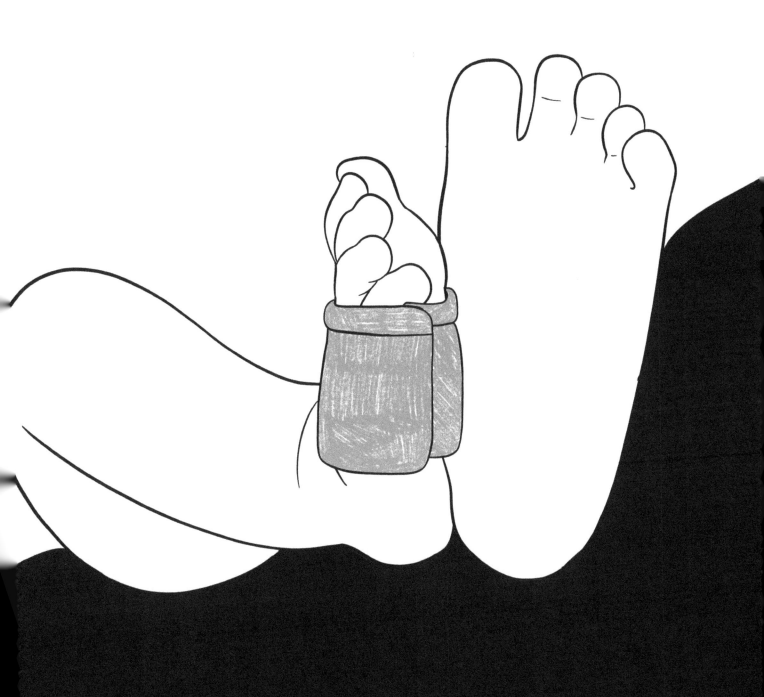

We witness your 'firsts'
in a space not our own.
Though to you, my little one,
this space feels like home.

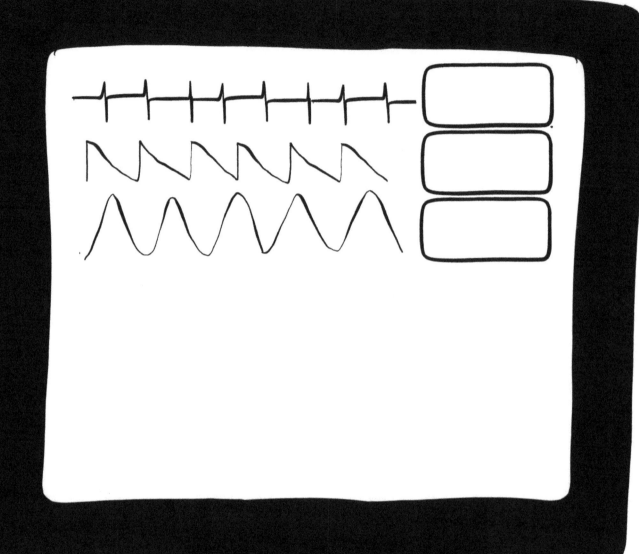

Healing takes time,
A lifetime's work in a day.

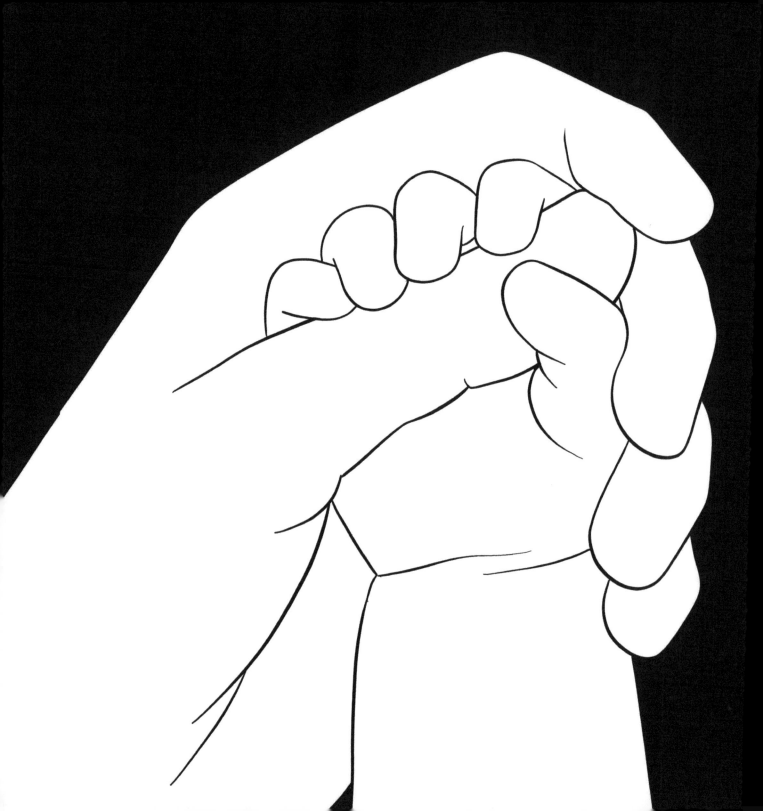

"You can. You will…

I'll be here,"
I say.

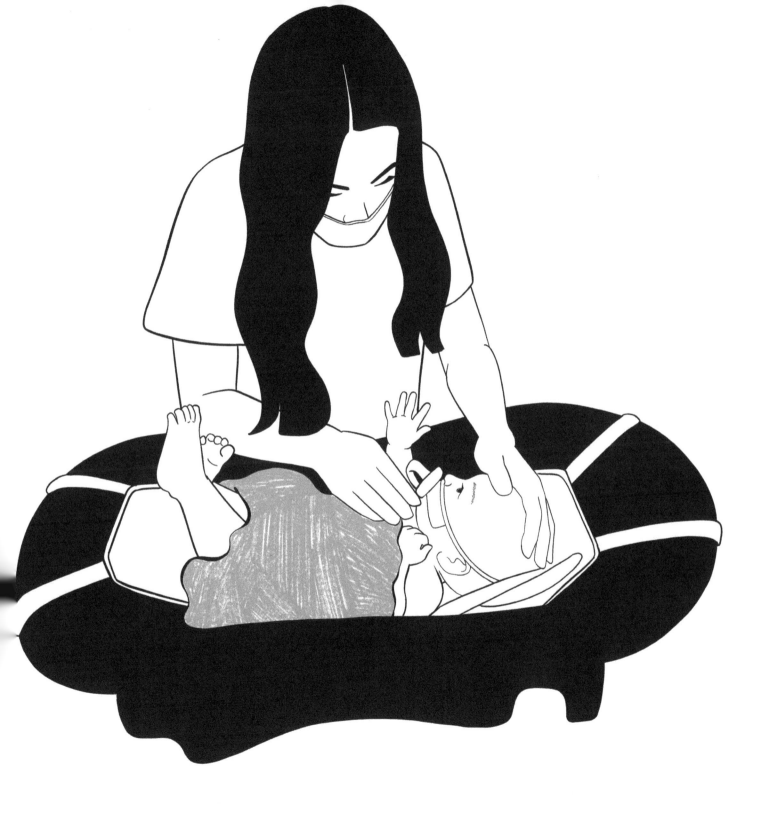

Our story is different,
as unique as they come.
This life you've been given
is a beautiful one.

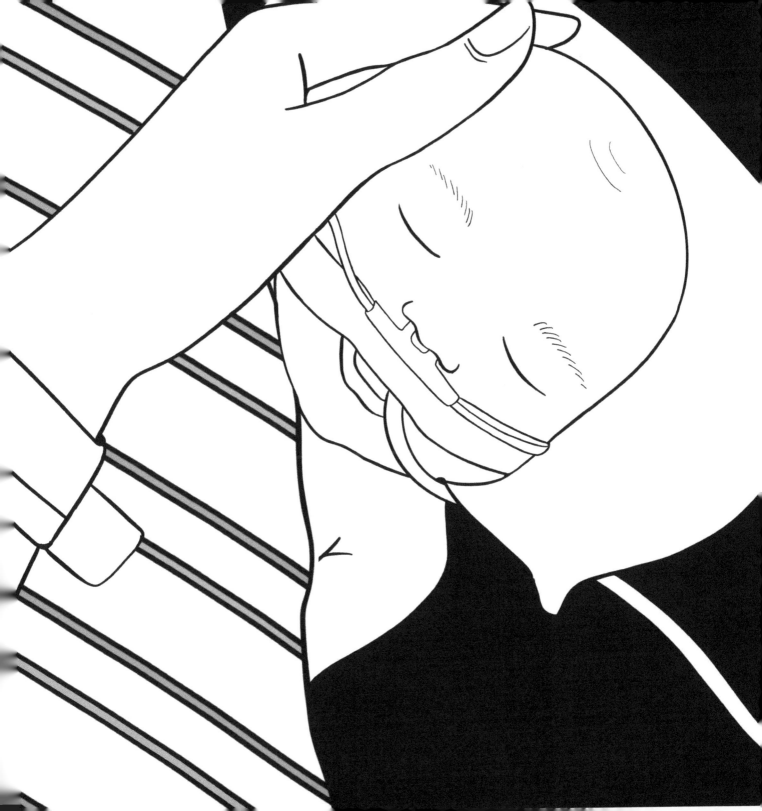

So show them you're ready
to come home and stay.
"One day at a time,"
they continue to say.

You'll grow and you'll thrive.
You will surprise us all.
Your strength is unmatched.
Your small body seems tall.

You will need doctors less.
You will need mama more.
"You are ready," they'll say
as we walk toward the door.

Welcome to the World,
my strong little one.
This is what I hoped for you.
Our next chapter has begun.

ABOUT THE AUTHOR

Shannon Kempton, a passionate special education teacher and advocate, holds academic credentials in Education, Writing Arts, and School Administration. Currently spearheading an Autism Program in Washington Township, New Jersey, her personal journey as a NICU mom inspired her to pen Our Story Is Different: A NICU Beginning. Shannon's son, Cameron, was diagnosed with a Lymphatic Conduction Disorder at birth and has been her prime motivation to reassure other NICU mothers and celebrate the formidable strength of NICU babies. Shannon lives with her husband, Steve, two sons, Donovan and Cameron, and their dog, Willow, in Washington Township.

SPECIAL ACKNOWLEDGEMENTS

Shannon would like to thank the following individuals for their important role in Cameron's Journey from the NICU to home: Dr. Yoav Dori, Ms. Erin Pinto NP, CHOP Lymphatics Team, and CHOP West 2 NIICU Nurses and Doctors.

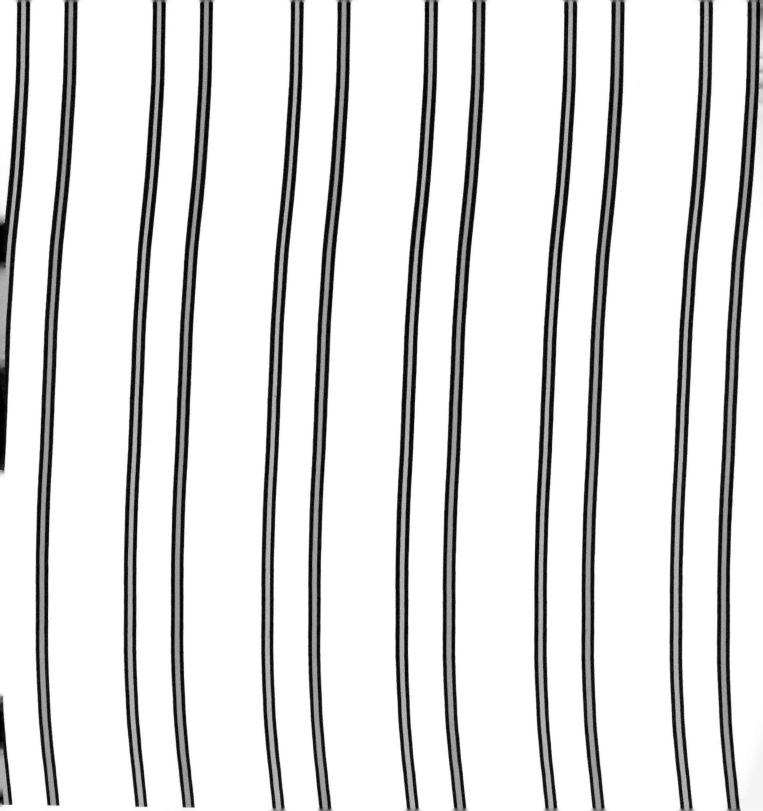

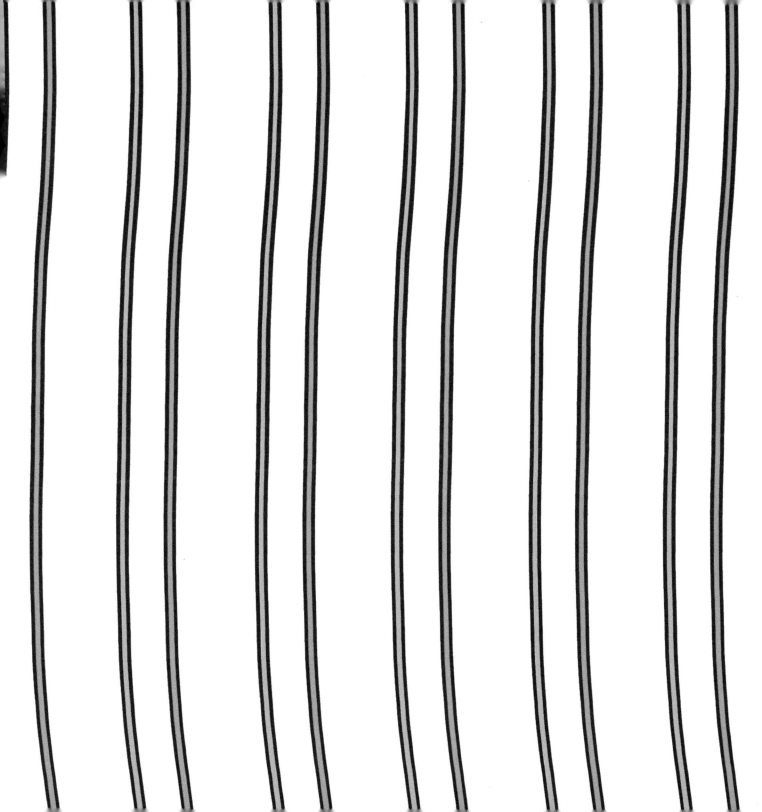

Printed in the USA
CPSIA information can be obtained
at www.ICGtesting.com
CBHW082326260124
3786CB00031B/1858